MW00490242

SING & LEARN
Phonics
VOL. 1

Ready-to-use reproducible worksheets and exercises
teaching short vowels, high-frequency consonants and blends

by Jack Brudzynski

Song lyrics: Ed P. Butts
Music: Sara Jordan (SOCAN)

ISBN: 978-1-55386-243-7

Acknowledgements

Author – Jack Brudzynski
Lyricist – Ed Butts
Composer – Sara Jordan (SOCAN)
Illustrator – Various Contributors
Educational Consultant – Arlene Grierson
Interior Layout – Darryl Taylor, Derek Veenhof
Cover Design – Campbell Creative Services
Editors – Joan Howard, Sara Jordan

For further information contact:

Jordan Music Productions Inc.
M.P.O. Box 490
Niagara Falls, NY
U.S.A. 14302-0490

Jordan Music Productions Inc.
R.P.O. Lakeport, Box 28105
St. Catharines, ON
Canada, L2N 7P8

Telephone: 1-800-567-7733
Web Site: www.sara-jordan.com
E-mail: sjordan@sara-jordan.com

We acknowledge the financial support of the Government of Canada through the Book Publishing Industry Development Program (BPIDP) for our publishing activities.

Canada

Table of Contents

ⓘ TIPS FOR THE TEACHER

Hints for Teachers and Parents

Welcome aboard! We're sure you'll enjoy our "Sing and Learn" Phonics series. This comprehensive, four-part series is presently used to teach school children all over the world to read and is now being used as far away as China!

Sing and Learn Phonics was developed using the Synthetic Phonics approach. Through this method of instruction, students are introduced to the 42 different sounds of letters and letter groups. They then practice reading, through the segmenting and blending of these sounds.

Comparative studies done of various phonics programs and methods prove that students learning to read using the Synthetic Phonics approach come out well ahead. To learn more about Sing and Learn Phonics and how it aligns with the Common Core Curriculum State Standards, please visit: SongsThatTeach.com/phonics.

The songs and activities in Volume One are based on short vowels, and high-frequency consonants. You will find that each lesson starts with two group activities. These group activities are followed by song lyrics (to be used with the accompanying CD to introduce each lesson's song).
Reproducible exercises based on the song conclude each chapter.

A few ways to use the songs, activities and exercises in this learning kit:

Before singing a song with students, we suggest that you announce the particular letter sounds to be learned that day, and have students practice identifying them in various words. Segment simple words into phonemes and then substitute new alternative phonemes to make new words. Simple c-v-c (consonant-vowel-consonant) words are used wherever possible. Studying phonics through song also utilizes the "whole language approach" allowing students to recognize sight words and to read words within the context of each song.

After a song has been sung, discuss with students what other new words they can think of that employ the same phonemes. Have students guess how these words are spelled. Advanced students will delight in using the music karaoke tracks allowing them to perform for the class or to write their own lyrics.
A word list, downloadable PDFs of picture cards, a supplemental worksheets and activities can be found by visiting our website: www.SongsThatTeach.com/phonics.

Learning to read can be an incredible journey for both student and teacher!

Sara Jordan

President

CHAPTER 1

Introducing the Alphabet

Letter-Picture Chain

Materials:
- picture cards
- scissors
- marker
- glue/tape

Preparation: Make word cards or print out word cards from our website at www.SongsThatTeach.com/bonus–materials.

How it Works: This activity will require picture cards. You can make your own from the "word list" on page 63, or print out the PDFs found at: www.SongsThatTeach.com/phonics. Cut each photocopied sheet of paper in half. Photocopy again, this time, half the page is blank. With a marker, draw the starting letter of the corresponding picture on the blank half. Cut out each picture and letter strip.

Sounds of the Alphabet

Materials:
- sticky–tack
- velcro or thumbtacks
- scissors
- bristol board X 2 (different colors)
- marker

Preparation: This activity will require picture cards. You can make your own from the "word list" on page 61, or print out the PDFs found at: www.SongsThatTeach.com/phonics. Cut out each picture and laminate (optional). Attach picture cards to a piece of bristol board and hang on the chalkboard. Cut the second bristol board into squares and write a letter corresponding to a picture on each square.

How it Works: There should be as many letter squares as picture cards used. Give each student a few letter squares. Say the sound of the picture on the picture board. The student with the correct letter square attaches their square on top of the corresponding picture.

The Letter Parade

chorus:

The alphabet is a letter parade,
a letter parade of sounds.
The alphabet is a letter parade,
a letter parade of sounds.
The alphabet is a letter parade,
a letter parade of sounds.
The alphabet is a letter parade,
a letter parade of sounds.

A cow has a name.
Do cows say "Cow"?
No! No!
Cows say "Moo".
A cat has a name.
Do cats say "Cat"?
No! No!
Cats say "Meow".

Letters have names
like A, B, C.
Letters have names
like D and E.
Letters have names
but they have sounds, too
like /ă/
in am,
and /d/ in do.

chorus:

The alphabet is a letter parade,
a letter parade of sounds.
The alphabet is a letter parade,
a letter parade of sounds.
The alphabet is a letter parade,
a letter parade of sounds.
The alphabet is a letter parade,
a letter parade of sounds.

Let's all sing the letters' names
then we can learn their sounds.

A B C D E F G
H I J K
L M N O P
Q R S T U V
W X Y and Z

We use letters and their sounds
to read all the words we see around.

Name: _____

Print the Alphabet

Trace each letter of the alphabet.

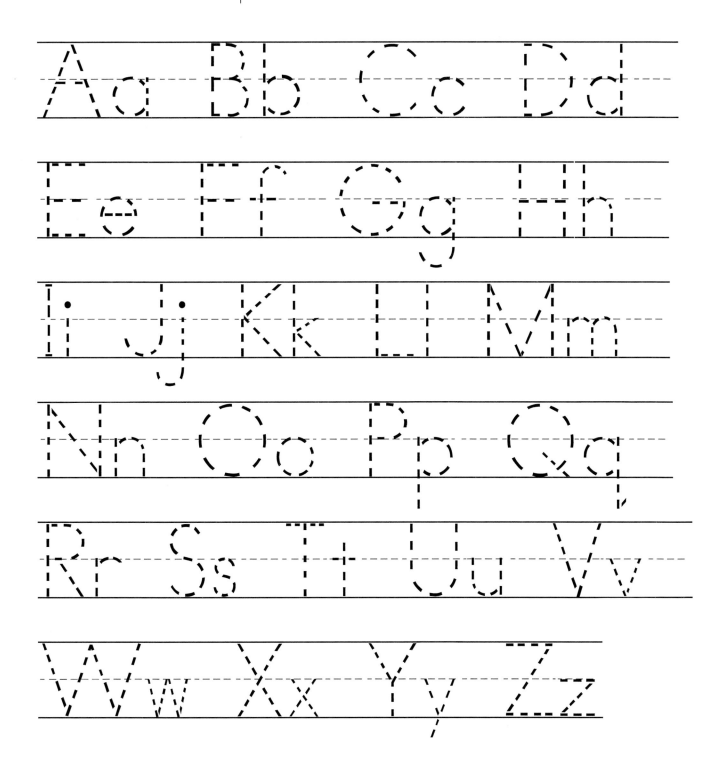

Starting Sounds

Sound out each picture. Trace the first letter of each picture.
Color all the pictures when finished.

b		bell
c		cake
d		dog
s		sun
p	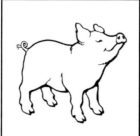	pig

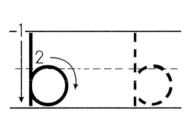
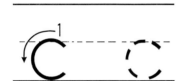
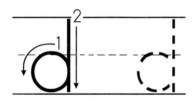
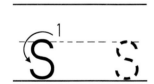
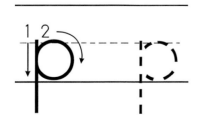
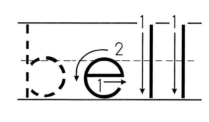

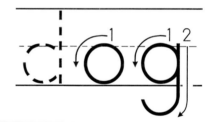

www.SongsThatTeach.com   Sing and Learn Phonics, vol. 1   © 2014 Sara Jordan Publishing

CHAPTER 2

Introduction to Vowels

Rhyming Picture Cards

Materials:
- rhyming picture cards
- scissors

Preparation: This activity will require picture cards. You can make your own from the "word list" on page 61, or print out the PDFs found at: www.SongsThatTeach.com/phonics. Laminate the picture cards.

How it Works: Each student receives a picture card. Students are to sound out their picture card with other classmates. They are to then form groups of rhyming picture cards. An alternate method of doing this activity would be to hold up a picture card and have the students determine whether their picture card rhymes with yours.

Vowel Recognition

Materials:
- bristol board
- ruler
- marker
- sticky–tack

Preparation: Create a 3 X 3 grid using the ruler on the bristol board. Create picture cards, laminate them and use sticky–tack or velcro to place them on the grid. While placing the pictures on the grid ask students whether the vowel in the word is making its sound or saying its name.

How it Works: By identifying whether vowels in words make their sound or say their name, students will be reminded that vowels are special letters capable of different sounds in different situations.

The Vowel Song

chorus:

We are special letters.
We're called vowels.
Let's call out our names.
Let's call out our names.
We are special letters.
We're called vowels.
Let's call out our names.
Let's call out our names.

a, e, i, o, and u... a, e, i, o, and u...
a, e, i, o, and u... and sometimes y.

a, e, i, o, and u... a, e, i, o, and u...
a, e, i, o, and u... and sometimes y.

Every word has a vowel.
It could be "a", "e" or "i".
Every word has a vowel.
It could be "o", "u" or "y".

chorus:

We are special letters.
We're called vowels.
Let's call out our names.
Let's call out our names.
We are special letters.
We're called vowels.
Let's call out our names.
Let's call out our names.

a, e, i, o, and u... a, e, i, o, and u...
a, e, i, o, and u... and sometimes y.

a, e, i, o, and u... a, e, i, o, and u...
a, e, i, o, and u... and sometimes y.

Sometimes vowels make short sounds.
The vowel "a" says /ă/ in pan.
Sometimes vowels say their names.
The vowel "a" says /ā/ in pane.

chorus:

We are special letters.
We're called vowels.
Let's call out our names.
Let's call out our names.
We are special letters.
We're called vowels.
Let's call out our names.
Let's call out our names.

a, e, i, o, and u... a, e, i, o, and u...
a, e, i, o, and u... and sometimes y.

a, e, i, o, and u... a, e, i, o, and u...
a, e, i, o, and u... and sometimes y.

Sing and Learn Phonics, vol. 1   © 2014 Sara Jordan Publishing

Missing Vowels

Sound out the picture. Which vowels say their name?
Trace the word and color the pictures with long vowel sounds.

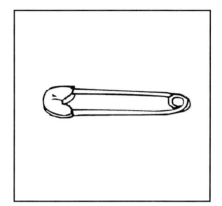

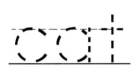

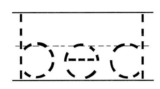

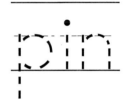

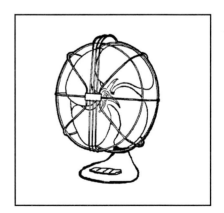

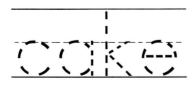

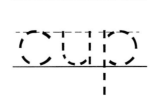

Cut and Paste: Rhyming Words

Sound out the pictures and color them. Cut out the pictures at the bottom of the page and paste them in the blank spaces. Trace the dotted words.

Trace the vowels with a colored pencil.

hat   bat   bag   flag

pen   ten   dog   frog

can   pan

Sing and Learn Phonics, vol. 1   © 2014 Sara Jordan Publishing

The Letter "s"

Silly "s" Stew

Materials:
- bristol board
- scissors
- marker
- pail

Preparation: Create a 3 x 3 grid on an 8" x 11" sheet of paper. Photocopy so that each student has a sheet. Students can draw silly foods that start with "s" that they'd like to add to the stew. Decorate a pail with festive colors and allow students to add their ingredients.

How it Works: Have each student take picture cards out of the stew and announce what the picture is, taking special care to sound out the "s" sound.

Sound Out the Word!

Materials:
- picture cards
- construction paper
- scissors
- glue, marker

Preparation : This activity will require picture cards. You can make your own from the "word list" on page 61, or print out the PDFs found at: www.SongsThatTeach.com/phonics. Cut out the pieces of construction paper a little larger than the picture cards. Write the corresponding word on the back of each picture card in its proper phoneme.
Laminate them (optional).

How it Works: Say or sing "This word sounds like /c/ /a/ /t/, can you guess the word?" Once the students have guessed the word, you can flip over the card to show the picture.
This activity could be done in small groups as well.

Swing, Swing Up (The Letter "s")

chorus 2x: 🎵

The letter "s" makes the sound /s/
like in see-saw, see-saw, see-saw.
The letter "s" makes the sound /s/
like in see-saw, swing and slide.

The letter "s" makes the sound /s/
like in see-saw, see-saw, see-saw.
The letter "s" makes the sound /s/
like in see-saw, swing and slide.

/s/ and ee, s-ee, see, /s/ and aw, s-aw, saw
You see me. I see you.
You saw me. I saw you too.

chorus 2x: 🎵

The letter "s" makes the sound /s/
like in see-saw, see-saw, see-saw.
The letter "s" makes the sound /s/
like in see-saw, swing and slide.

The letter "s" makes the sound /s/
like in see-saw, see-saw, see-saw.
The letter "s" makes the sound /s/
like in see-saw, swing and slide.

/s/ and wing, s-wing, swing
/s/ and lide, s-lide, slide
You swing me. I'll swing you.
You slide first then I'll slide too.

chorus 2x: 🎵

The letter "s" makes the sound /s/
like in see-saw, see-saw, see-saw.
The letter "s" makes the sound /s/
like in see-saw, swing and slide.

The letter "s" makes the sound /s/
like in see-saw, see-saw, see-saw.
The letter "s" makes the sound /s/
like in see-saw, swing and slide.

Swing, swing up. Slide, slide down.
See-saw, see-saw up and down.
Swing, swing up. Slide, slide down.
See-saw, see-saw up and down.

chorus 2x: 🎵

The letter "s" makes the sound /s/
like in see-saw, see-saw, see-saw.
The letter "s" makes the sound /s/
like in see-saw, swing and slide.

Sing and Learn Phonics, vol. 1 © 2014 Sara Jordan Publishing

Coloring the Scene: "Ss"

Color all of the items in the scene that start with the /s/ sound.

Cut out the scene when finished.

How many items did I color?   _____

Name: _____

Missing Letters: "Ss"

Sound out each picture. Fill in the missing letter.

Trace each word and color the pictures that have an /s/ sound.

 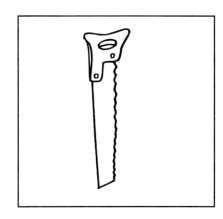 

 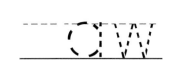 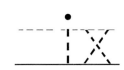

_un _aw _ix

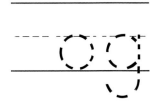 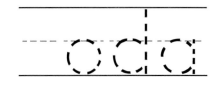 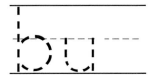

_og _oda bu_

www.SongsThatTeach.com

Sing and Learn Phonics, vol. 1   © 2014 Sara Jordan Publishing

CHAPTER 4

The Short "a"

Robot Talk

Materials:
- picture cards
- scissors

Preparation: This activity will require picture cards. You can make your own from the "word list" on page 63, or print out the PDFs found at: www.SongsThatTeach.com/phonics. Laminate them (optional).

How it Works: Explain to the students that robots do not think and are programmed to pronounce every sound in order to say a word. Announce: "It's Robot-Time!" Hold up picture cards which include the sound of the short "a" and have the students read it out slowly, pronouncing every sound just like a robot would.

Picture Popcorn

Materials:
- picture cards
- scissors
- timer (optional)

Preparation: This activity will require picture cards. You can make your own from the "word list" on page 63, or print out the PDFs found at: www.SongsThatTeach.com/phonics. Only cut out the pictures that have a short "a" sound in them (optional). Laminate them (optional).

How it Works: Give each student a picture card while the class sits in a circle. Give students a moment to look at their pictures and sound out the words. When everyone is ready, one student stands up, says his/her word and sits back down. The adjacent student does the same and so on until every student in the circle has had a turn. Then, each student passes his/her picture card to the left, right or across and play again. A timer can be used as an extra challenge.

Fat Cat (Short "a")

chorus 2x: 🎵

The sound of the short "a" is /ă/,
/ă/, /ă/, /ă/.
/ă/ is the first sound in: am and at.
/ă/ is the middle sound in:
man, had, fat, cat, mad, sad, black, hat.
/ă/, /ă/, /ă/

The sound of the short "a" is /ă/,
/ă/, /ă/, /ă/.
/ă/ is the first sound in: am and at.
/ă/ is the middle sound in:
man, had, fat, cat, mad, sad, black, hat.
/ă/, /ă/, /ă/

s–a–d, s–a–d, s–a–d, sad
m–a–d, m–a–d, m–a–d, mad
f–a–t, f–a–t, f–a–t, fat
s–a–t, s–a–t, s–a–t, sat.

A man had a cat. The cat was fat.
That cat would soon flatten his hat.
The cat sat on the man's black hat.
The man said, "I am mad at my cat."
"Cat on the hat. You've flattened my hat.

Now my hat is flat, flat, flat."
"Stand up cat, you silly, silly cat.
You go back to your cat mat."

chorus 2x: 🎵

The sound of the short "a" is /ă/,
/ă/, /ă/, /ă/.
/ă/ is the first sound in: am and at.
/ă/ is the middle sound in:
man, had, fat, cat, mad, sad, black, hat.
/ă/, /ă/, /ă/

Name: _____

Cut and Paste: Apple Tree of "a"s

Color all of the items in the scene that start include a short /ă/ sound.

Cut out the scene when finished.

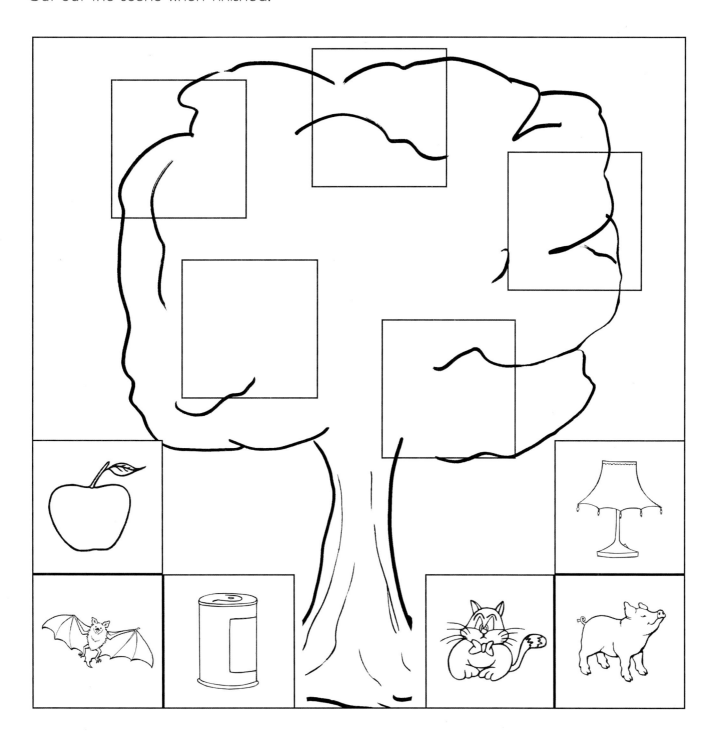

Missing Letters: "Aa"

Sound out each picture. Fill in the missing letter. Trace each word.
Color the pictures that have a short "a" sound.

The Letter "m" and the Short "a"

Word S-T-R-E-T-C-H

Materials: Picture cards, scissors, marker

Preparation: This activity will require picture cards. You can make your own from the "word list" on page 63, or print out the PDFs found at: www.SongsThatTeach.com/phonics. Cut out each picture card and write the corresponding words on the back of each picture card with a marker.

How it Works: Showing the word (not picture), have the students guess the word as you slowly pronounce each sound. Once the students have guessed correctly, you may flip over the card and show the picture

My G-o-o-o-e-y Pizza

Materials: Picture Cards, bristol board X number of groups scissors, sticky–tack, glue

Preparation: Divide class into groups (2–8 people per group). This activity will require picture cards. You can make your own from the "word list" on page 63, or print out the PDFs found at: www.SongsThatTeach.com/phonics. Using scissors, cut out the picture cards and one large circle on each bristol board.

How it Works: Give each group of children 4–16 picture cards so that they can glue them on their pizzas. Once finished, you ask the students what's on their pizza!
(i.e. "What's on your pizza Tom?" Jam, J–a–m, Jam is on your pizza!)
Challenge: Have the groups exchange pizzas before presenting.

CHAPTER 5

"m" and Short "a" Sam the Man

chorus: 🎵

The letter "m" makes the sound:
/m/, /m/, /m/.
"m" says /m/,
m–a–n man.

The short vowel "a" makes the sound:
/ă/, /ă/, /ă/.
"a" says /ă/,
a–m am.

m–a–n, m–a–n
m–a–n, man
a–m, a–m
am, am, am.

Sam is a man;
a man, man, man.
Sam likes ham
and Sam likes jam.

Ham and jam,
jam and ham,
Ham and jam
for Sam, Sam, Sam.

chorus: 🎵

The letter "m" makes the sound:
/m/, /m/, /m/.
"m" says /m/,
m–a–n man.

The short vowel "a" makes the sound:
/ă/, /ă/, /ă/.
"a" says /ă/,
a–m am.

M–a–p, m–a–p,
m–a–p, map
m–a–t, m–a–t,
m–a–t, mat.

Sam has a map,
a map, map, map.
Sam, Sam sat
on a mat with his map.

Map and mat,
mat and map;
a map and a mat
for Sam, Sam, Sam.

chorus: 🎵

The letter "m" makes the sound:
/m/, /m/, /m/.
"m" says /m/,
m–a–n man.

The short vowel "a" makes the sound:
/ă/, /ă/, /ă/.
"a" says /ă/,
a–m am.

Color the "m" and Short "a"

Sound out each picture. Color the pictures that have an "m" or short "a" sound.

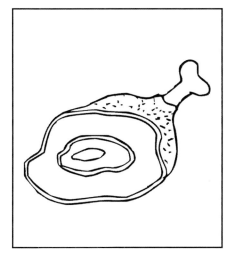

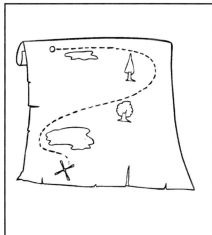
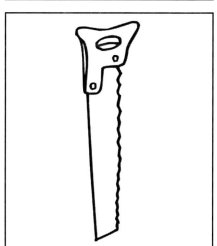

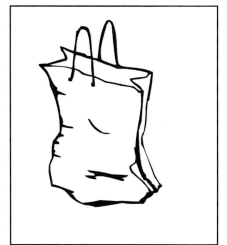

Sam's Can of Jam

Help Sam choose biscuits to eat with his jam. Choose biscuits with the short "a" sound.
Color the ones you have chosen.

Sing and Learn Phonics, vol. 1 © 2014 Sara Jordan Publishing

CHAPTER 6

The Short "u"

Punch-It-Out

Materials:
- picture cards
- scissors

Preparation: This activity will require picture cards. You can make your own from the "word list" on page 63, or print out the PDFs found at: www.SongsThatTeach.com/phonics. Cut them out. Laminate them (optional).

How it Works: Focus on targetting the sound of short "u". You as well as the students move their palms to each sound and punch when hearing the target "u".

Rhyming Picture Chain

Materials:
- picture cards,
- glue

Preparation: This activity will require picture cards. You can make your own from the "word list" on page 63, or print out the PDFs found at: www.SongsThatTeach.com/phonics. Cut them out. Laminate them (optional). Divide the class up into groups.

How it Works: Give each group a set of picture cards with the short "u" sound and give each group a several other picture cards having sounds other than the short "u" sound. Have the children make a chain of rhyming picture cards only having the short "u" sound. They can then color them and present them to you by saying what each picture is. Every word should rhyme.

Bud the Duck (Short "u")

chorus 2x: 🎵

The sound of the short vowel "u" is: /ŭ/,
/ŭ/, /ŭ/, /ŭ/, /ŭ/.
The sound of the short vowel "u" is: /ŭ/,
/ŭ/, /ŭ/, /ŭ/, /ŭ/.

The sound of the short vowel "u" is: /ŭ/,
/ŭ/, /ŭ/, /ŭ/, /ŭ/.
The sound of the short vowel "u" is: /ŭ/,
/ŭ/, /ŭ/, /ŭ/, /ŭ/.

/ŭ/ is the first sound in: up.
/ŭ/ is the middle sound in:
Bud, mud, yuck, luck,
muck, stuck, lucky duck,
dug, bug, hum, yum,
buzz.......

B–u–d, B–ud, Bud
m–u–d, m–ud, mud
l–u–ck, l–uck, luck
d–u–ck, d–uck, duck.

Bud the duck dug in the mud.
The lucky duck dug up a bug.
The bug said, "Buzz." The bug said, "Hum."
Bud said, "Bugs are yum, yum, yum."

The bug said to Bud, "Put me down, Duck.
Bugs are not yum. Bugs are yuck."
Bud put the bug in the muck, muck, muck,
but now Bud was stuck, stuck, stuck.

chorus 2x: 🎵

The sound of the short vowel "u" is: /ŭ/,
/ŭ/, /ŭ/, /ŭ/, /ŭ/.
The sound of the short vowel "u" is: /ŭ/,
/ŭ/, /ŭ/, /ŭ/, /ŭ/.

The sound of the short vowel "u" is: /ŭ/,
/ŭ/, /ŭ/, /ŭ/, /ŭ/.
The sound of the short vowel "u" is: /ŭ/,
/ŭ/, /ŭ/, /ŭ/, /ŭ/.

Sing and Learn Phonics, vol. 1   © 2014 Sara Jordan Publishing

Bud the Duck and his Friends

Color Bud the Duck, his friends and their surroundings.

Short "u" items – brown.

Short "a" items – green.

Color the rest of the items red.

Word bank				
duck	bug	ball	mud	hat
cat	sun	wagon	bell	web

Missing Letters: "Uu"

Sound out each picture. Fill in the missing letter. Trace each word.
Color the pictures that have a short "u" sound.

 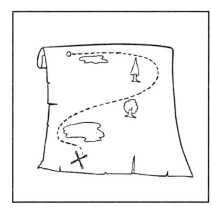 

 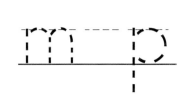 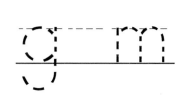

 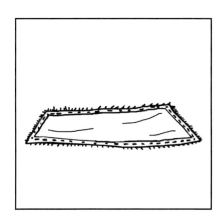 

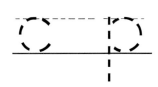 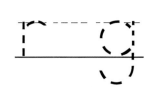 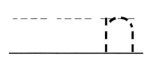

Sing and Learn Phonics, vol. 1   © 2014 Sara Jordan Publishing

CHAPTER 7

The Letters "h" and "p"

Stand-Up, Sit-Down!

Materials:
- picture cards,
- scissors

Preparation: This activity will require picture cards. You can make your own from the "word list" on page 63, or print out the PDFs found at: www.SongsThatTeach.com/phonics Cut them out and laminate (optional).

How it Works: Split the class up into two or more groups. Designate a letter of the alphabet to each group – in this case we'll use "H" and "P". Read out words and hold up the corresponding picture card. If an "H" sound was heard, the H group should stand up (or raise their hands). If a "P" sound was heard, the P group should stand up. If both sounds are heard, both groups stand-up. If none of the designated sounds are heard, none of the groups should stand-up.

Continuous Song of Sounds

Materiales: none

Preparación: none

Así funciona: Sing "Hi", and students respond with "Pi". Then sing "Ho", and students respond with "Po", and so on. To make it more challenging and more fun, add more sounds to be repeated such as "Hi Ho", and students respond "Pi Po". "Hi Ho Hum", and students respond "Pi Po Pum". This activity can be changed for any starting sound especially the ones that were already introduced in previous exercises.

Huff and Puff ("h" and "p")

chorus 2x:

The letter "h" makes the sound: /h/, /h/, huff.
The letter "p" makes the sound: /p/, /p/, puff.
h–uff, huff, p–uff, puff,
h–uff, huff, Huff and puff a song.
h–uff, huff, p–uff, puff,
h–uff, huff, Huff and puff a song.

The letter "h" makes the sound: /h/, /h/, huff.
The letter "p" makes the sound: /p/, /p/, puff.
h–uff, huff, p–uff, puff,
h–uff, huff, Huff and puff a song.
h–uff, huff, p–uff, puff,
h–uff, huff, Huff and puff a song.

/h/, /h/, /h/, /h/, hen, hen
In the /p/, /p/, pen, pen
/h/, /h/, /h/, /h/, ham, ham
in the /p/, /p/, pan, pan.

/p/, /p/, /p/, /p/, pot, pot.
The pot is /h/, hot, hot.
/p/, /p/, pigs and puppies play.
Ho, ho, ho, ho, Hey, hey, hey!

chorus:

The letter "h" makes the sound: /h/, /h/, huff.
The letter "p" makes the sound: /p/, /p/, puff.
h–uff, huff, p–uff, puff,
h–uff, huff, Huff and puff a song.
h–uff, huff, p–uff, puff,
h–uff, huff, Huff and puff a song.

Sing and Learn Phonics, vol. 1 © 2014 Sara Jordan Publishing

Cut and Paste: Sorting Cans

Sound out all the pictures and color them. Cut and paste the pictures with a "h" sound into the "h" can and the pictures with a "p" sound into the "p" can.

Coloring the Scene: "Hh" and "Pp"

Help Harry Huff and Puff a song. Color the words beginning with "h" red.
Color the words beginning with "p" blue. Color all other words yellow.

How many items did I color?   _____

Sing and Learn Phonics, vol. 1   © 2014 Sara Jordan Publishing

CHAPTER 8

The Letters "b" and "t"

Cookie Hunt

Materials: picture cards, brown construction paper, scissors, glue

Preparation: This activity will require picture cards. You can make your own from the "word list" on page 63, or print out the PDFs found at: www.SongsThatTeach.com/phonics.
Cut out as many circles from the brown construction paper as possible. Make sure they are big enough for a picture card to be glued onto them. Paste the picture cards on the "cookies". Laminate (optional).

How it Works: Hide the cookies throughout the room. Have the students find as many cookies as they can and return them to the cookie jar. Before the cookies go into the cookie jar, the student must say what kind of cookie is going in.
Eg: "What's going into the cookie jar?"
       "A g–u–m cookie is going in the cookie jar".

T-T-T-T-T-TRAIN!!!

Materials : picture cards, scissors, construction paper in many different colors, sticky–tack or thumbtacks

Preparation: This activity will require picture cards. You can make your own from the "word list" on page 63, or print out the PDFs found at: www.SongsThatTeach.com/phonics.
Cut out many rectangles from the colored construction paper to be used as train cars. Attach the train cars to the board.
Note: The train could get longer everyday!

How it Works: Rant:
"Chug–a–chug–a–choo–choo, my train spells words.
This word sounds like /p/ /i/ /g/ – chug–a–chug–a–choo–choo.
What does that spell?" (Students say – "Pig")
"Pig! – a pig is on my train!
What else is on my train travelling today?
Continue to with other words as a student attaches the picture card to a train car. Song ends with: "And that is all that's on my train travelling today".

B-Bop-B and Toe-Tap-T ("b" and "t")

chorus:

The letter "b" makes the sound:
/b/, /b/, /b/, b–bop–b.
The letter "t" makes the sound:
/t/, /t/, /t/, toe–tap–t.
B–bop–b, toe–tap–t;
bop and tap to "b" and "t".

/b/, /b/, b–bop, big boots brown
/t/, /t/, tap ten toes to town
/t/, /t/, toe–tap, two tall trees
/b/, /b/, b–bop, birds and bees
/b/, /b/, b–bop, big blue bell
/t/, /t/, toe–tap, time to tell.

chorus:

The letter "b" makes the sound:
/b/, /b/, /b/, b–bop–b.
The letter "t" makes the sound:
/t/, /t/, /t/, toe–tap–t.
B–bop–b, toe–tap–t;
bop and tap to "b" and "t".

/b/, /b/, b–bop, big black bug
/t/, /t/, toe–tap, tag, tip, tug
/t/, /t/, toe–tap, tic–tac–toe
/b/, /b/, b–bop, bag of bows
/t/, /t/, toe–tap, try, try, try
/b/, /b/, b–bop, bye, bye, bye.

chorus:

The letter "b" makes the sound:
/b/, /b/, /b/, b–bop–b.
The letter "t" makes the sound:
/t/, /t/, /t/, toe–tap–t.
B–bop–b, toe–tap–t;
bop and tap to "b" and "t".

Missing Letters: "Bb" and "Tt"

Sound out each picture. Fill in the missing letter. Trace each word.
Color the pictures that have a "b" or "t" sound .

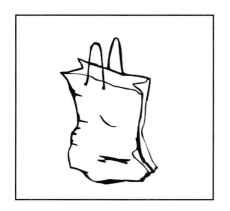
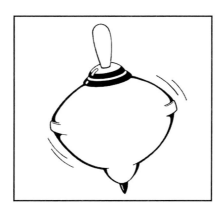
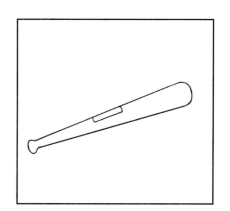

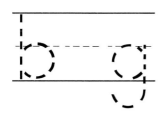
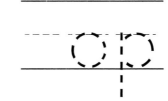
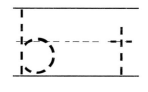

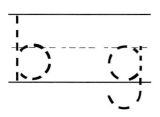

B-Bop Dancers' Balloons

Color each of Billy's and Tina's balloons red if they contain words with a "b" sound.

Color their balloons blue if they contain words with a "t" sound.

Color the balloons yellow if they have both "b" and "t" sounds.

The Short "e"

Clowns

Materials: picture cards, many colored sheets of construction paper or real balloons, scissors, glue, sticky-tack or masking tape.

Preparation: This activity requires picture cards. You can make your own from the "word list" on page 63, or print out the PDFs found at: www.SongsThatTeach.com/phonics. Cut out colored balloon-shaped pieces of construction paper and paste the picture cards on them or tape the picture cards to the real balloons.

How it Works: Split the class into two groups. Give each group a sound, such as the short e or short a sound. Tape the balloons on the chalkboard. Ask students to read out only the words that have their designated sound. If a student from a group sounds out a word correctly with their designated sound, the group takes the balloon. The group with the most balloons at the end wins.

Show and Tell

Materials: picture cards, white construction paper, scissors, glue, marker

Preparation: This activity will require picture cards. You can make your own from the "word list" on page 63, or print out the PDFs found at: www.SongsThatTeach.com/phonics. Cut out and paste the picture cards on pieces of construction paper leaving about 2" of excess construction paper at the bottom to write the word with a marker. Write the word with one vowel missing.

How it Works: Draw all the vowels on the board. Raise a picture card with a vowel missing and have a student go to the board, choose the correct vowel and pronounce the word. Repeat this activity with the rest of the class.

9 | CHAPTER 9

Jen's Pet Hen (Short "e")

chorus 2x: 🎵

The short vowel "e" makes the sound: /ĕ/.
The first sound of elephant.
The short vowel "e" makes the sound: /ĕ/.
The first sound of elephant.

/ĕ/ is the middle sound of: Jen, hen, pen.
/ĕ/ is the middle sound of: fell, sell, well.
/ĕ/ is the middle sound of: vet, pet, wet.
/ĕ/ is the middle sound of: let, get, set.

The short vowel "e" makes the sound: /ĕ/.
The first sound of elephant.
The short vowel "e" makes the sound: /ĕ/.
The first sound of elephant.

/ĕ/ is the middle sound of: Jen, hen, pen.
/ĕ/ is the middle sound of: fell, sell, well.
/ĕ/ is the middle sound of: vet, pet, wet.
/ĕ/ is the middle sound of: let, get, set.

J–e–n, J–e–n, J–en, Jen
p–e–n, p–e–n, p–en, pen
g–e–t, g–e–t, g–et, get
w–e–t, w–e–t, w–et, wet.

Jen has a hen. The hen is her pet.
Jen let her pet hen get all wet.
Wet, wet, the hen is wet.
Jen has a wet, pet hen.

chorus: 🎵

The short vowel "e" makes the sound: /ĕ/.
The first sound of elephant.
The short vowel "e" makes the sound: /ĕ/.
The first sound of elephant.

/ĕ/ is the middle sound of: Jen, hen, pen.
/ĕ/ is the middle sound of: fell, sell, well.
/ĕ/ is the middle sound of: vet, pet, wet.
/ĕ/ is the middle sound of: let, get, set.

Jen let the hen go to the well.
In the well the pet hen fell.
Jen put the hen in the pen
and sent for the vet to check on her pet.

chorus: 🎵

The short vowel "e" makes the sound: /ĕ/.
The first sound of elephant.
The short vowel "e" makes the sound: /ĕ/.
The first sound of elephant.

/ĕ/ is the middle sound of: Jen, hen, pen.
/ĕ/ is the middle sound of: fell, sell, well.
/ĕ/ is the middle sound of: vet, pet, wet.
/ĕ/ is the middle sound of: let, get, set.

Cut and Paste: Susan's Shopping Cart

Sound out all the pictures and color them. Susan is shopping for the short "e" sound.
Cut and paste the pictures with a short "e" sound into Susan's shopping cart.

Jen and Her Pet Hen

Jen is in the top left hand corner and her hen is in the bottom right hand corner.
Help Jen get to her pet hen by coloring the short "e" words to form a pathway.

Sing and Learn Phonics, vol. 1 © 2014 Sara Jordan Publishing

CHAPTER 10

The Short "o"

The Hungry "o" Monster!

Materials: Picture cards, construction paper, marker.

Preparation: This activity will require picture cards. You can make your own from the "word list" on page 63, or print out the PDFs found at: www.SongsThatTeach.com/phonics.
Paste the picture cards on construction paper leaving enough room at bottom to write the corresponding word.

Optional: Create monster face out of excess paper.

How it Works: Start with simple c–v–c words and increase later during the activity.
Rant:
"The Hungry "o" Monster is hungry for some dog, d–o–g"
Students: "/d/ yum /g/ gulps the Hungry "o" Monster"
"...rubbing his belly and wiping his mouth"
Repeat until "The Hungry "o" Monster is full with o's"
(Change to another vowel).

Kindergarten Zoo

Materials: Note: Could be called Grade # Zoo as well. Picture cards, big piece of bristol board, marker, masking tape/ sticky–tack.

Preparation: This activity will require picture cards. You can make your own from the "word list" on page 63, or print out the PDFs found at: www.SongsThatTeach.com/phonics.
Cut out only the picture cards with animals on them. Write large single letters of the alphabet (not neccesarily all of them) on the bristol board.

How it Works: Spread out picture cards on the floor or table and have each student take one or a few depending on how many there are. Each student attaches the animal under the correct letter on the bristol board while sounding out its name. If the animal doesn't have a corresponding letter, then they sound out the name of the animal and say: "There is no place for (animal) in our Kindergarten Zoo!".

Tom Hops (Short "o")

chorus 2x:

The short vowel "o" makes the
sound: /ŏ/, /ŏ/, /ŏ/, /ŏ/.
The short vowel "o" makes the
sound: /ŏ/, /ŏ/, /ŏ/, /ŏ/.

/ŏ/ is the first sound in: on.
/ŏ/ is the first sound in: off.
/ŏ/ is the middle sound in:
Tom, socks, pot, hot
hop, stop, top, not.

The short vowel "o" makes the
sound: /ŏ/, /ŏ/, /ŏ/, /ŏ/.
The short vowel "o" makes the
sound: /ŏ/, /ŏ/, /ŏ/, /ŏ/.

/ŏ/ is the first sound in: on.
/ŏ/ is the first sound in: off.
/ŏ/ is the middle sound in:
Tom, socks, pot, hot
hop, stop, top, not.

o–n, o–n, o–n, on
T–o–m, T–o–m, T–om, Tom
t–o–p, t–o–p, t–op, top
n–o–t, n–o–t, n–ot, not.

Tom hops and hops on top of his cot.
Hops a lot on top of his cot.
Tom's socks are on, Tom's socks are off.
Tom cannot hop if his socks are off.

chorus:

The short vowel "o" makes the
sound: /ŏ/, /ŏ/, /ŏ/, /ŏ/.
The short vowel "o" makes the
sound: /ŏ/, /ŏ/, /ŏ/, /ŏ/.

/ŏ/ is the first sound in: on.
/ŏ/ is the first sound in: off.
/ŏ/ is the middle sound in:
Tom, socks, pot, hot
hop, stop, top, not.

Tom's dog hops on a box, box, box.
Tom's dog cannot hop in his socks.
Tom and his dog cannot stop.
Tom's Mom yells, "Don't hop on the cot."

chorus:

The short vowel "o" makes the
sound: /ŏ/, /ŏ/, /ŏ/, /ŏ/.
The short vowel "o" makes the
sound: /ŏ/, /ŏ/, /ŏ/, /ŏ/.

/ŏ/ is the first sound in: on.
/ŏ/ is the first sound in: off.
/ŏ/ is the middle sound in:
Tom, socks, pot, hot
hop, stop, top, not.

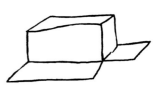

Name: _____

Color the "o"

Sound out all the pictures and color them.

Sound out each picture. Color the pictures that have a short "o" sound.

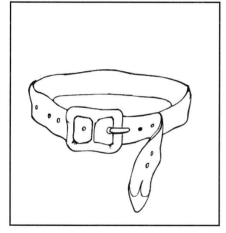

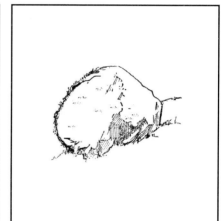

"Spot", the Boxer Dog

Tom's dog Spot deserves some treats. Tom will give him bones that have short "o" words. How many can you find? Color them.

Sing and Learn Phonics, vol. 1 © 2014 Sara Jordan Publishing

The Letters "n" and "r"

The Sounds on the Wheel Go Round

Materials: Picture cards (could be of just "n" and "r" words), cardboard, bristol board, stick or piece of wood, thumbtack and scissors.

Preparation: Cut out two identical circles – one of cardboard, the other from bristol board. Glue stick to cardboard circle. Print the picture cards found on our website, cut them out and paste them to perimeter of cardboard. Cut out a picture card sized hole on the perimeter of bristol board. Attach bristol board to cardboard using a thumbtack allowing it to spin.

How it Works: Sing: "The sounds of the wheel go round and round, round and round, round and round. The sounds of the wheel go round and round, until we stop at:"
Wheel stops exposing a picture card and students sound out the word. Repeat.

What's the First Sound That You Hear?

Materials: None

Preparation: Prepare a list of 4-word phrases such as:
Dark, doll, dog and daddy
Sock, sun, sea and snake
Moon, mouse, mop and milk
Ant, answer, add and apple

How it Works: To the tune of *London Bridge is Falling Down*, sing: "What's the first sound that you hear in dark, doll, dog and daddy?"
Students sing back:
"The first sound that we hear is /d/ /d/ "D".
Note: When students reply, they are to sound out the first two /d/s, and say the letter "D" at the end.

CHAPTER 11

Nell and Rob ("n" and "r")

chorus:

The letter "n" makes the sound:
/n/, /n/, /n/, /n/.
The letter "n" makes the sound:
/n/, /n/, /n/, /n/.
N–e–ll, N–e–ll, N–e–ll, Nell.
N–e–ll, N–e–ll, N–e–ll, Nell.

The letter "r" makes the sound:
/r/, /r/, /r/, /r/.
The letter "r" makes the sound:
/r/, /r/, /r/, /r/.
R–o–b, R–o–b, R–o–b, Rob.
R–o–b, R–o–b, R–o–b, Rob.

n–o–d, nod, n–o–t, not,
n–a–p, nap, N–e–ll, Nell,
r–u–n, run, R–o–b, Rob,
r–a–n, ran, r–o–t, rot.

Nelly likes "n" words:
nod, nod, Nell.
Nelly likes "n" words:
nod, nod, Nell.

Robby likes "r" words:
run, run, Rob.
Robby likes "r" words:
run, run, Rob.

chorus:

The letter "n" makes the sound:
/n/, /n/, /n/, /n/.
The letter "n" makes the sound:
/n/, /n/, /n/, /n/.
N–e–ll, N–e–ll, N–e–ll, Nell.
N–e–ll, N–e–ll, N–e–ll, Nell.

The letter "r" makes the sound:
/r/, /r/, /r/, /r/.
The letter "r" makes the sound:
/r/, /r/, /r/, /r/.
R–o–b, R–o–b, R–o–b, Rob.
R–o–b, R–o–b, R–o–b, Rob.

Cut and Paste: What's in the Nest?

Sound out all the pictures and color them.

Cut and paste the pictures with a "n" or "r" sound into the nest.

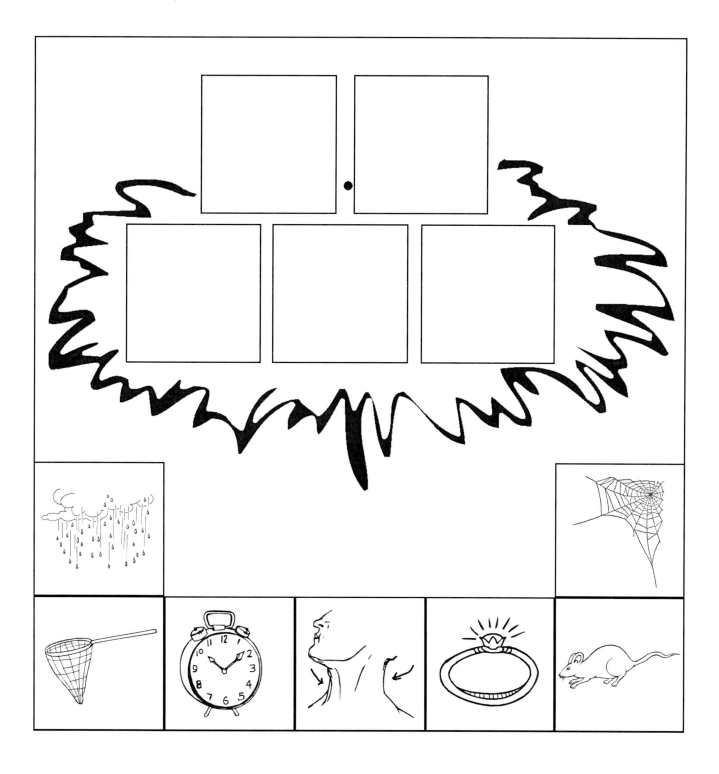

Color the Rain Drops

Sound out each picture. Color the rain drops with the "n" sound blue. Color the rain drops with the "r" sound green. Color the rest in colors of your choice.

Sing and Learn Phonics, vol. 1 © 2014 Sara Jordan Publishing

CHAPTER 12

The Short "i"

Picture Puzzle

Materials:
- picture cards
- scissors
- marker

Preparation: This activity will require picture cards. You can make your own from the "word list" on page 63, or print out the PDFs found at: www.SongsThatTeach.com/phonics. Optional – cut out only the pictures with a short "i" sound. Cut up the each picture card into the number of phonemes. Write the corresponding phoneme on the back of each piece.

How it Works: Mix up all the pieces and place them on a table. A student is asked to take a piece and find the rest. Once the student finds all the pieces and starts putting each piece together, ask them to pronounce each phoneme as they assemble their picture puzzle and say the entire word once the puzzle is complete.

Kick-box Phonics

Materials:
- picture cards
- scissors

Preparation: This activity will require picture cards. You can make your own from the "word list" on page 63, or print out the PDFs found at: www.SongsThatTeach.com/phonics. Cut them out. Laminate (optional).

How it Works: Select a phoneme, such as d. Select all the picture cards containing the sound of d in them. Read out the word while the students break it down into its proper phonemes and:

"Punch out" the d if it is at the beginning of the word,

"Kick down" the d if it is at the end of the word and

"Push over" the d if it is in the middle of the word.

Jill and Bill (Short "i")

chorus 2x: 🎵

The short vowel "i" sounds like this:
/ ĭ /, / ĭ /, / ĭ /, / ĭ /.
The short vowel "i" sounds like this:
/ ĭ /, / ĭ /, / ĭ /, / ĭ /.

/ ĭ / is the first sound of: if, in, it, is.
/ ĭ / is the middle sound of:
Jill, Bill, will, hill, sit, with, him.

The short vowel "i" sounds like this:
/ ĭ /, / ĭ /, / ĭ /, / ĭ /.
The short vowel "i" sounds like this:
/ ĭ /, / ĭ /, / ĭ /, / ĭ /.

/ ĭ / is the first sound of: if, in, it, is.
/ ĭ / is the middle sound of:
Jill, Bill, will, hill, sit, with, him.

I–f, i–f, i–f, if
J–i–ll, J–i–ll, J–i–ll, Jill
B–i–ll, B–i–ll, B–i–ll, Bill
h–i–ll, h–i–ll, h–i–ll, hill.

If Jill sees Bill sit on the hill,
Jill will sit with Bill.sit on the hill,
Jill will sit with Bill.

If Jill has milk to sip with Bill,
she won't let it spill.Jill will sip with Bill.
Sip milk on the hill.

chorus 2x: 🎵

The short vowel "i" sounds like this:
/ ĭ /, / ĭ /, / ĭ /, / ĭ /.
The short vowel "i" sounds like this:
/ ĭ /, / ĭ /, / ĭ /, / ĭ /.

/ ĭ / is the first sound of: if, in, it, is.
/ ĭ / is the middle sound of:
Jill, Bill, will, hill, sit, with, him.

The short vowel "i" sounds like this:
/ ĭ /, / ĭ /, / ĭ /, / ĭ /.
The short vowel "i" sounds like this:
/ ĭ /, / ĭ /, / ĭ /, / ĭ /.

/ ĭ / is the first sound of: if, in, it, is.
/ ĭ / is the middle sound of:
Jill, Bill, will, hill, sit, with, him.

Sing and Learn Phonics, vol. 1 © 2014 Sara Jordan Publishing

Jill and Bill

Jill and Bill are sitting on a hill. They are sorting pictures that have a short "i".
Help them by coloring the pictures that have a short "i" sound.

Name: _____

Missing Letters: "Ii"

Sound out each picture. Fill in the missing letter. Trace each word.
Color the pictures that have a short "i" sound.

p _ n   _ x   w _ g

_ g   _ r   _ ps

CHAPTER 13

The Letters "c" and "d"

Spider Web

Materials: Picture cards, scissors, 2 balls of yarn, hole-punch

Preparation: This activity will require picture cards. You can make your own from the "word list" on page 63, or print out the PDFs found at: www.SongsThatTeach.com/phonics. Laminate and punch two holes at the top of each picture card. Using the first ball of yarn, create necklaces by weaving yarn through the two holes and tying the ends together.

How it Works: Ask the class to sit in a circle. Each student receives a number of necklaces. The activity begins by rolling the second ball of yarn to a student. That student is then asked to sound out the word on the necklace and roll the ball to anyone else. Repeat until the ball of yarn runs out.
A different spider web forms each time!

The Longest Earthworm

Materials: Picture cards, brown construction paper, scissors masking tape

Preparation: This activity will require picture cards. You can make your own from the "word list" on page 63, or print out the PDFs found at: www.SongsThatTeach.com/phonics. Cut out two picture card-wide wavy strips of brown construciton paper as the bodies for two earthworms. Any excess construction paper can be used to create heads.

How it Works: Tape the two earthworm heads on the chalkboard as well as one strip of the body to each head. Divide the class into two equal groups – each having their own worm. Sound out a letter. Each group must sift through the pile of picture cards looking for words that contain that sound and tape it to their worm. Once their worm is full, attach another body strip to the end of the worm. Repeat until all picture cards have been attached to the worms.
Who has the longest worm?

Come On Over ("d" and Hard "c")

The hard sound of "c" sounds like this:
/k/, /k/, /k/.
The letter "d" sounds like this:
/d/, /d/, /d/.

cat, call, can, clock
They start with the sound: /k/, /k/.
dot, dad, day, dog
They start with the sound: /d/, /d/.

The hard sound of "c" sounds like this:
/k/, /k/, /k/.
The letter "d" sounds like this:
/d/, /d/, /d/.

cat, call, can, clock
They start with the sound: /k/, /k/.
dot, dad, day, dog
They start with the sound: /d/, /d/.

c–a–t, cat, c–a–n, can
d–o–g, dog, D–a–n, Dan.

chorus:

Come on over. Come and play.
Come on over any day.

We can do the can–can like in days of old.
Dressing up in costumes and in old clothes.

chorus:

Come on over. Come and play.
Come on over any day.

We can cook dinner, cake and cookies too.
Come on over we've so much to do.

chorus:

Come on over. Come and play.
Come on over any day.

When the clock says that the day is done,
can you come again? We'll have lots of fun.

chorus 2x:

Come on over. Come and play.
Come on over any day.

Come on over. Come and play.
Come on over any day.

Come on over. Come and play.

Missing Letters: "Cc" and "Dd"

Sound out each picture. Fill in the missing letter. Trace each word.
Color the pictures that have a "c" or "d" sound.

Cancan Dancing

The can can dancers are having a party! Color each item:

– red, if it begins with a "c" sound.

– green, if it begins with a "d" sound.

– blue, if it begins with any other sound..

Sing and Learn Phonics, vol. 1 © 2014 Sara Jordan Publishing

CHAPTER 14

The Letters "f" and "l"

Stand-Up, Sit-Down!

Materials:
- picture cards
- scissors

Preparation: This activity will require picture cards. You can make your own from the "word list" on page 63, or print out the PDFs found at: www.SongsThatTeach.com/phonics. Cut them out. Laminate (optional).

How it Works: Split the class up into two or more groups. Designate a letter of the alphabet to each group – in this case we'll use "h" and "p". Read out words and hold up the corresponding picture card. If a "h" sound was heard, the h-group should stand-up (or raise their hands). If a "p" sound was heard, the p-group should stand-up. If both sounds are heard, both groups stand-up. If neither of the designated sounds are heard, neither of the groups should stand-up.

Raise your Flag

Materials:
- colored construction paper
- two paint–stirring sticks or similar object
- markers
- accompanying songbook or children's book

Preparation: Split the materials into two groups.

How it Works: Divide the class into two groups. One group will be the f–sounds group, the other the l–sounds group. Have each group create their own flag labeled with its designated sound ("f" or "l"). Read out pieces from a children's book or the "f and l" song on the accompanying songbook and have each group raise its flag when the students hear their sound.

The Frog and the Lad ("f" and "l")

chorus 2x:

The letter "f" sounds like this: /f/, /f/, /f/.
The letter "f" sounds like this: /f/, /f/, /f/.
It's the first sound of: fat, frog, fall
and the middle of: craft, left, gift
and the last sound of: loaf, stuff, sniff
/f/, /f/, /f/.

The letter "l" sounds like this: /l/, /l/, /l/.
The letter "l" sounds like this: /l/, /l/, /l/.
It's the first sound of: log, look, like
and the middle of: melt, salt, milk
and the last sound of doll, will, fall
/l/, /l/, /l/.

l-o-g, log, f-o-g, fog
f-a-d, fad, l-a-d, lad

A fat, fat frog falls off a log,
off a log, in the fog.

A little lad looks at the frog,
by the log, in the fog.

The frog likes the lad, the lad likes the frog,
a lad and a frog by a log in the fog.

chorus 2x:

The letter "f" sounds like this: /f/, /f/, /f/.
The letter "f" sounds like this: /f/, /f/, /f/.
It's the first sound of: fat, frog, fall
and the middle of: craft, left, gift
and the last sound of: loaf, stuff, sniff
/f/, /f/, /f/.

The letter "l" sounds like this: /l/, /l/, /l/.
The letter "l" sounds like this: /l/, /l/, /l/.
It's the first sound of: log, look, like
and the middle of: melt, salt, milk
and the last sound of doll, will, fall
/l/, /l/, /l/.

Sing and Learn Phonics, vol. 1 © 2014 Sara Jordan Publishing

Sorting Cans

Sound out all the pictures and color them. Cut and paste the pictures with a "f" sound into the "f"– can and the pictures with a "l" sound into the "l"– can.

"f" or "l"? Which is it?

Sound out each picture. Determine whether the picture has an "f" sound or an "l" sound.
Draw the correct letter under the picture.

Sing and Learn Phonics, vol. 1 © 2014 Sara Jordan Publishing

Picture cards for the word list, supplementary phonics worksheets and activities can be found on our website at: www.sara-jordan.com/phonics

angel	cave	feather	jail	oyster	scooter	teeth
ant	celery	feet	jam	page	scream	ten
ape	cereal	fence	jar	pail	seven	tent
apple	chain	fern	jelly	pan	shark	thief
arm	chair	fire	jet	park	sheep	thin
ask	cheese	fish	jug	pay	shell	think
baby	chicken	five	juggle	peach	ship	thirty
bag	chimney	flag	juice	pen	shirt	thorn
basket	church	flame	ketchup	pencil	shoes	three
bat	cigar	flashlight	key	pie	shout	ticket
bat	city	flea	kick	pig	shower	toad
bath	claw	flower	king	pin	sigh	top
beach	cloak	flute	kite	pizza	sing	toys
bean	clock	food	knee	plane	six	tractor
bed	closet	football	knight	plant	skate	train
bee	cloud	forest	knob	plate	skunk	trash
bell	clover	fork	knock	pliers	sky	tree
belt	clown	fox	ladder	plum	sled	troll
bench	coat	frog	lamp	pocket	sleep	truck
bike	coin	gate	leaf	poison	sleigh	trunk
bird	cone	gem	leg	pool	slide	tub
blanket	cord	giant	light	pot	small	tube
blocks	corn	giraffe	lion	price	smile	turtle
boat	couch	girl	lips	prince	smoke	umbrella
bone	crab	globe	lock	print	snail	van
book	cradle	glue	log	prize	snake	vet
boots	crane	goat	look	propeller	sneeze	vine
box	crayon	gong	lung	quail	snore	wagon
boy	crib	grape	mail	quake	snow	wall
branch	cricket	grass	map	queen	soap	watch
bread	crown	gravy	marker	quick	socks	wave
brick	cry	grill	mask	quill	soda	web
bridge	cube	guitar	mice	quit	soil	whale
broom	cup	gum	milk	quiz	space	wheat
bug	cymbals	ham	mirror	race	spider	wheel
bunny	day	hammer	mole	rain	spoon	whip
burger	deer	hand	moon	rake	spy	whistle
bus	ding-dong	hanger	mop	rat	squid	wig
bush	dinosaur	happy	mouse	right	stage	wings
cage	dog	harp	mule	ring	stairs	winter
cake	doll	hat	neck	rock	star	wood
can	dragon	hay	necklace	rocket	stick	x-ray
candle	dress	hen	nest	rose	sun	yak
candy	drink	high	net	rug	swamp	yarn
cane	drum	hook	night	sailor	swan	yawn
cap	duck	horn	nose	saw	sweater	yo-yo
car	egg	horse	nurse	scale	swim	zoo
carpet	fan	house	nuts	scarecrow	swing	
castle	farm	ice	oil	scarf	tape	
cat	farmer	jacket	owl	school	teacher	

Ask your retailer about other excellent titles by teacher, Sara Jordan!

Sing and Learn Sight Words Series – Aligned with Common Core Curriculum State Standards

This comprehensive four-part series introduces students to over 300 of the most commonly used sight words. It has been created for students from K–3 but would be useful for beginning readers of any age. The series is based on the list of 200 frequently used service words compiled by Edward William Dolch, Ph.D., and the related list of 95 high-frequency nouns. Series includes 50 songs, 50 karaoke tracks, 100 group activities, and hundreds of reproducible exercises   K–Gr. 3

Sing and Learn Phonics – Aligned with Common Core Curriculum State Standards

Blending the best in educational research and practice, this four-part series is a structured program providing students with the strategies needed to decode words through rhyming, blending and segmenting. Each learning kit includes songs, karaoke tracks, group activities and dozens of reproducible exercises. K–Gr. 2

Math Unplugged Series – Aligned with Common Core Curriculum

This four part series teaches addition, subtraction, multiplication and division while pulling in relevant strands of the Common Core Math Curriculum. Each learning kit includes an audio song CD with an added bonus of self-quizzing tracks. The 64 page reproducible resource book contains song lyrics, group activities and individual exercises.

Visit us online to shop, listen and learn.

Our websites, www.SongsThatTeach.com and www.AprendeCantando.com, offer:
- an opportunity to purchase our resources online
- a biweekly newsletter including free songs,   downloads and activities
- free worksheets based on our educational songs,
  which may be printed and shared with your class
- cartooning lessons, pen pal exchanges and contests
- healthy snack ideas
- information regarding educational standards
- links to other valuable websites

For further information or to request a free catalog, please call us toll-free at:
1-800-567-7733 or e-mail: info@sara-jordan.com

Sara Jordan Publishing
M.P.O. Box 490
Niagara Falls, NY
U.S.A. 14302-0490

Sara Jordan Publishing
R.P.O. Lakeport, Box 28105
St. Catharines, Ontario
Canada, L2N 7P8